my happy place

**A POSITIVE PSYCHOLOGY-BASED GUIDED
JOURNAL TO HELP YOU LIVE YOUR BEST LIFE**

THE SKILL COLLECTIVE

about

THE SKILL COLLECTIVE

At The Skill Collective we help build skills for a better life in the areas of wellbeing, mental health, and performance. We draw on evidence-based research and our experience as psychologists to translate science into easy, practical tips. Check out our website (www.theskillcollective.com).

COPYRIGHT + TERMS OF USE

DISCLAIMER

ISBN 978-0-6453375-1-8 in hardcover print format.
1 2 3 4 5 6 7 8 9 `10

The Skill Collective
www.TheSkillCollective.com

my happy place

contents

8
what is
positive psychology?
Learn about 5 key
concepts from positive
psychology that will help
you to thrive in life.

92
maintaining wellbeing
in challenging times
Handle setbacks and thrive in
times of adversity by building
grit and resilience.

18
set up for success
Here are our key tips
to turn journalling into
a habit.

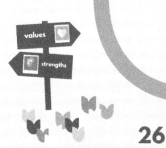

26
your best life starts here
Find the path to your happy place. Lean into
your values, flex your strengths, and stop and
smell the roses using mindfulness and gratitude.

110
uplifting moments
Boost your positive emotions
when it matters - awe, happiness,
and contentment all help to
broaden awareness and build
new ways to thrive.

160
references
+ resources

155
where to from here?
Continue your progress with tips to
keep you journalling beyond your
30-day My Happy Place journey.

124
flourishing in life
Take the leap from feeling good
to building enduring happiness
and flourishing in life.

how to use this journal

Thirty days to a happier place?
Use this guided journal to kick start your
journey. Through intentional, mindful practice,
regular journalling can help you to move
towards long-lasting positive changes.

The prompts in this journal are drawn from
positive psychology, a branch of psychology
devoted to helping you thrive in life.

the aim of
positive psychology
is to **catalyse a change**
in psychology from a preoccupation
only with **repairing the
worst things in life**
to also **building the
best qualities in life.**

- martin seligman -

what is
positive psychology?

Positive psychology represents a shift from the more traditional focus of psychology on bouncing back from setbacks to flourishing in life. There are concepts within positive psychology that help you to live your best life, and the prompts in My Happy Place are drawn from these ideas. In this section we cover our favourite five:

1. Happiness

Happiness may be the final destination, but what path do you take to get there? Martin Seligman, father of positive psychology, noted three routes to happiness:

The first is a pleasant life, in which you pursue experiences and things that bring pleasure. This may look like doing retail therapy, having a massage, or eating a favourite food.

An engaged life is the second path to happiness, where you use your strengths and virtues to get into a state of flow. Engagement might look like having passion for your work or for pursuing hobbies.

A meaningful life is the third path to happiness, in which you use your strengths and virtues in service of something that is greater than yourself. In doing so, you fill your life with what really matters.

Of these three routes, it's a meaningful life that makes the largest contribution to enduring happiness. What makes life meaningful, however, differs for everyone. For some, it's about striving for justice, whereas for others it may be about helping those in need. The key is to uncover what matters to you.

happiness
is not

something
readymade.

it comes
from your
own actions.

-jim rohn-

2. PERMA or PERMA-H

Martin Seligman identified five essential elements to resilience and wellbeing, forming the PERMA model. This consists of: Positive Emotions, Engagement, Positive Relationships, Meaning, and Accomplishment. A sixth pillar, Health, was added more recently to this model. Let's take a closer look at each of these.

Positive emotions are essential to wellbeing, and include not only happiness but also joy, contentment, and gratitude. By experiencing positive emotions you not only feel better, you also enhance creativity and boost problem-solving skills.

Engagement occurs when you are fully immersed in an activity that uses your strengths, skills, and focus. Being in a state of flow is a sign of engagement.

Humans are social creatures, and feeling connected through positive relationships is vital to wellbeing and to protection from challenges.

A meaning-filled life fosters wellbeing as you work towards a purpose that is larger than yourself, akin to a life compass.

Accomplishments in life provide a sense of mastery as you strive towards goal attainment.

Physical health is vital to happiness and wellbeing. Good nutrition, adequate sleep, and exercise are essential to good physical health, a clear mind, and emotion regulation.

We'll dive deeper into PERMA-H on page 134.

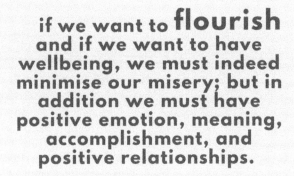

if we want to **flourish**
and if we want to have
wellbeing, we must indeed
minimise our misery; but in
addition we must have
positive emotion, meaning,
accomplishment, and
positive relationships.

the skills and exercises
that build these are
entirely different from the
skills that minimise our
suffering.

-martin seligman -

3. Strengths + Virtues

Strengths and virtues relate to those positive traits that you can flex to enhance wellbeing, live a more engaged and meaningful life. They can take you from merely surviving to thriving, helping you to flourish. There are six overarching virtues (endorsed across different cultures) under which sit 24 strengths. On the next page we outline these virtues and strengths.

Everyone has a different profile of strengths. We recommend that you take the Values in Action (VIA) Strengths Survey to identify your main strengths.

wisdom

The pursuit of this virtue involves obtaining and using knowledge. Strengths under this virtue include a love of learning, open-mindedness, curiosity, and creativity.

courage

This virtue relates to the pursuit of goals in the face of obstacles. Under this virtue are strengths such as bravery, perseverance, zest, and honesty.

humanity

The virtue of humanity centres on relationships and humankind. Strengths under this virtue include kindness, love, as well as social and emotional intelligence.

justice

A sense of justice, or civic-mindedness, promotes a healthy community. Fairness, leadership, and teamwork are examples of strengths under this virtue.

temperance

Temperance relates to self-control and protects against excesses in life. Strengths under this virtue include forgiveness, prudence, and self-regulation.

transcendence

Transcendence refers to a connection to the universe and beyond. It includes strengths like spirituality, hope, and an appreciation of beauty and excellence.

4. Grit

Grit is the passion and perseverance for long-term goals, particularly in the face of challenges. Those with grit are more resilient and better able to bounce back from adversity.

Individuals with grit also report higher levels of happiness and life satisfaction, as well as better mental health.

Grit can be increased through a shift in mindset, learning from setbacks, and through intentional practice. Grit can also be enhanced by taking stock of successive small wins - doing so helps to increase motivation and stay on track with longer-term goals.

success doesn't
just happen.

it is a product of
hard work, grit,
and ingenuity.

- ogwo david emenike -

5. Gratitude

Gratitude refers to the expression of thanks for things in life and a deep appreciation of life as being of meaning and value.

Feeling grateful shifts your focus towards the glass as being half full and turns the volume down on your negative emotions. Practising gratitude can also help you to find silver linings during tough times.

Through intentional and regular gratitude practice you cultivate greater appreciation for what you have and, in turn, enhance your happiness and wellbeing.

even in
the chaos of
everyday
life,

moments
of gratitude
remind us to
hold on to
the good
things.

- brit morin -

set up for success

how to make journalling a habit

It may feel exciting to start something new, but sticking to a habit requires planning, practice, perseverance, and a bit of science know-how. Here are our favourite tips:

the centre of your universe

To reap the full benefits of journalling, make it the centre of your universe. That is, journal when you're free from distractions such as friends, devices, and background noise. You can also focus better when you set aside stress and to-do lists.

feel good for follow through

You're more likely to stick to a habit when you find it intrinsically rewarding. That is, the reward comes from within, such as feeling satisfied or content. Thankfully, the prompts contained in My Happy Place are designed to dial up the feel-good factor.

caring for your environment

Engineer your environment to enhance the appeal of journalling. Perhaps set up a cosy nook at home, place this journal somewhere prominent, and keep your favourite pen together with this journal. The more enticing your environment is, the more likely you are to stick with journalling.

repetition is key

Forming habits essentially boils down to repeating something over and over again. The key is learning how to sustain motivation when you hit a wall. Find a way to stay on track with your new habit, whether it's by stacking journalling on top of an existing habit (such as brushing your teeth) or by setting yourself reminders.

get into the groove

Create a routine around journalling. If you prefer to journal in the morning, start the day off with your morning coffee, sit on the balcony, and focus on the journal prompt of the day before moving on to the rest of your morning routine.

Alternatively, if journalling at night is more your thing, you could do it at the end of your bedtime routine after brushing your teeth and before turning the lights out.

rise up to the challenge

If accountability means that you're more likely to stick to journalling, why not commit to working through My Happy Place with a friend? You can also increase accountability by putting your intention to journal out there.

Over the next couple of pages, list specific actions that you will take to help you stay on track with journalling.

actions for journalling

a goal without a plan is just a wish.

- antoine de saint-exupery -

writing in a journal each day allows you to direct your focus to what you accomplished, what you're grateful for

and what you're
committed to
doing better
tomorrow.
thus you more
deeply enjoy
your journey
each day.

- hal elrod -

are you ready?

Your journey to a happier place starts right here! This section looks at visualising your best possible self, and helps you to get there by identifying your strengths and clarifying your values.

Ways to reach your happy place are also covered in this section. Acts of kindness (and other prosocial behaviours), living mindfully, and practising gratitude all serve to enhance wellbeing.

a happier place

starts here

1 Write a letter titled "Dear best possible self"

Writing to the best version of your future self increases positive emotions such as happiness and optimism, and provides a guiding path for your way forward. For this exercise:

- Choose a future time in your life (say, 6 months, a year, 10 years even), and visualise your life as if you were living it in the moment.

- Describe your environment in detail – where you live, where you work or study, and your community. Engage your senses for this, detailing the sights, smells, and sounds of your environment.

- Describe important friendships and relationships in this time. How do you connect with others? How do you spend your time with them?

- Describe your day from the moment you wake up to the moment you close your eyes at night.

- Note the strengths that you draw upon as you live your life as your best possible self.

values are like fingerprints. nobody's are the same, but you leave 'em all over everything you do.

- elvis presley -

2 What are 3 values that are important to you? Why are they important?

value 1

value 2

value 3

What matters to people? A global survey by the World Economic Forum of over half a million people (encompassing 152 languages), found the 10 most commonly endorsed values to be:

1. Family
2. Relationships
3. Financial security
4. Belonging
5. Community
6. Personal growth
7. Loyalty
8. Religion/spirituality
9. Employment security
10. Personal responsibility

The global pandemic put these values in sharp focus - social isolation and travel restrictions highlighted just how important family, relationships, community, and a sense of belonging are to everyone.

if you want
to feel rich,
just count
the things
you have
that money
can't buy.

- allec mallanao -

3 How can you become more aligned in your values and actions?

It's easy to take action without thinking about the direction in which you are headed. Reflecting on your actions these past few weeks, how well did they align with what's important to you? What can you do to be more aligned with your values?

when values,
thoughts, feelings,
and actions are
in alignment, a
person becomes
focused and
character is
strengthened.

- john c maxwell -

VIA character strengths
turning values into action

It's one thing to hold values. It's another to act in a way that is aligned with them.

Martin Seligman and Christopher Peterson developed a framework of six virtues and 24 character strengths to represent 'values in action' (VIA), with the view that flexing these character strengths enables the pursuit of a meaningful and fulfilling life.

As with the World Economic Forum's cross-cultural study of values (see page 36), there are strengths that are universally endorsed.

A longitudinal study of strengths spanning 10 years and 75 nations, totalling over a million adults, identified those strengths most (and least) commonly endorsed by people all around the world.

most endorsed	least endorsed
honesty	self-regulation
fairness	modesty
kindness	prudence
judgement	spirituality
curiosity	zest

How can you translate values into meaningful action? First, identify your strengths (take the VIA Strengths Survey). Next, set goals around those strengths that you'd like to work on. Then, find ways to incorporate these into daily life. Some examples of how to achieve this include:

- The strength of fairness may be translated into daily action by treating people equally and checking your unconscious biases.

- The strength of curiosity can be exercised by signing up for something new or exploring the 'why' behind a phenomenon.

- The strength of open-mindedness can be flexed by viewing a situation through different lenses.

- The strength of self-regulation can be applied by practising emotion regulation skills.

Use the next few pages to reflect on your character strengths and how you can flex them.

4

What do you think some of your strengths are? How do you use these in your daily life?

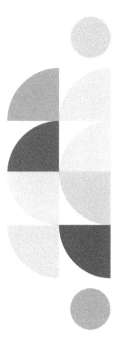

the good life is using your
signature strengths every day
to produce authentic happiness
and abundant gratification.

- martin seligman -

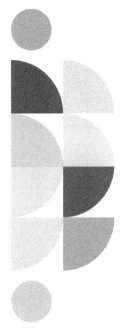

helping others

Shower someone with **kindness** and reap the benefits for your wellbeing and happiness.

Indeed, research shows that flexing this character strength (which sits under the virtue of humanity) for even just seven days leads to increased happiness.

Acts of kindness can be for the benefit of others (for example, volunteering), or for yourself. Research also shows that:

- Acts of kindness directed at yourself (such as self-care) boost your wellbeing. However, a larger wellbeing boost is observed when your acts of kindness benefit others. These, and other forms of **prosocial behaviours** (such as sharing) have beneficial side effects including a boost in your mood and an increase in feeling socially connected.

- Even the act of remembering a kind act that you previously performed increases your positive emotions.

volunteering

With so many benefits to volunteering, from boosting your wellbeing, becoming more social, increasing a sense of belonging, and enhancing life satisfaction, why not sign up to do your bit for a meaningful cause?

random acts of kindness

A random act of kindness can make a big difference to someone's day and fill you with compassion and satisfaction. Here are some examples of acts of kindness to help you flex this character strength:

- Connecting through conversation.
- Randomly giving someone a compliment.
- Shopping locally and supporting a small business.
- Giving up your seat to someone who needs it.
- Donating, be it food to someone in need, or your time to a worthy cause.
- Shipping someone a care package.
- Paying it forward.

acts of kindness

**no act of
kindness,
no matter
how small,
is ever
wasted.**

- aesop -

5 **Think back to a time when you've helped someone.**

Deep-dive into this moment, journaling about the event and its impact on you and the person you helped.

stop and smell the roses

As you move towards a more meaningful life, it helps to stop and smell the roses. This next section helps you to do just that, with a range of exercises to boost your wellbeing and make your heart sing.

There is an emphasis on gratitude in this section as the act of appreciation does wonders for your wellbeing.

The act of stopping and smelling the roses also requires mindfulness, which helps you to focus on the here and now rather than on the worries in your mind.

mindful
moments

Since mindfulness leapt onto
our collective radars it's been
touted as a magic elixir that
soothes troubles and boosts
wellbeing.

These claims are backed by
science - studies show that
mindfulness improves stress,
anxiety, and depression.

Neuroimaging studies show
that mindfulness shifts the
focus of attention away from
the self, reduces rumination,
and helps with emotion
regulation.

Let's dive deeper into the
impact of mindfulness.

mindfulness means paying attention in a particular way: on purpose, in the present moment, and non-judgementally.

- jon kabat-zinn -

When you're mindful you focus on the present moment and on input from your senses. This helps you to detach your focus from the worries in your mind and from the next item on your never-ending to-do list.

Mindfulness encourages you to reflect rather than to judge, to pause and notice your internal experience in response to what is happening externally. In turn, rather than running on autopilot, you can:

- Tune in to thoughts, observing them rather than judging and reacting to them.

- Sit with strong emotions and, instead of defaulting to unhelpful behaviours, you can choose to respond in healthier ways.

mindfulness is a pause - the space between stimulus and **response**: that's where choice lies.

- tara brach -

different ways to be mindful

Mindfulness is a way of life, and there are many ways in which to be mindful. Below are just some ideas for getting your daily dose of mindfulness.

- **Mindfulness meditation** is what is commonly associated with mindfulness practice - a type of meditation focusing on what you feel and sense in the moment. **Mindful breathing** (focusing on the sensation of the breath as you inhale and exhale) and **body scan meditation** (focusing on sensations in the body) are common types of mindfulness meditation.

- **Mindful walking** encourages you to tune in to movement within your body, and to drink in your surroundings. These actions help your mind to disengage from mental chatter.

- **Mindful communication** happens when you practise **mindful listening**, drawing on non-judgemental curiosity in response to what you hear, what your thoughts tell you, and on your emotions. In doing so, you can choose to respond in a less reactive and more intentional manner.

Reflecting on mindful experiences after the fact (for example, via journalling!) can further help you to maximise your experience.

6 Set your timer for 10 minutes.
Write whatever comes to mind, without
censoring or judging what you've written.

Following these 10 minutes, reflect on what you've written.

I became aware of:

I was surprised by:

I wonder about:

This stream of consciousness activity helps you to unload what's on your mind and to sift through your many thoughts and emotions.

7

How does your body feel right now?

Close your eyes for 5 minutes and focus on all of the sensations that you feel in your body from the top of your head all the way down to your toes. When these 5 minutes are up, journal about what you noticed.

My body feels...

Physical health is a recent, and important, addition to Martin Seligman's PERMA-H wellbeing model. Looking after the body through movement, a nutritious diet, and a stable sleep routine, are all crucial to positive wellbeing and mental health.

In spite of recognising the importance of good health, sometimes it's hard to tune out the external noise in our busy lives in order to really listen to what our body needs. Today's journal prompt includes a mindfulness exercise to help you hone in on subtle messages that your body may have for you.

8

Set your timer for 5 minutes for this exercise. Your task is to spend your time mindfully colouring the picture on the next page. Draw on all of your senses during this task, and if your mind wanders, redirect it to the task at hand. After 5 minutes, write down what you noticed whilst doing this exercise.

gratitude

gratitude

Through appreciating what's good in your life, rather than focusing on what's missing, you can lift your mood even in challenging times.

Gratitude practice can take on different forms, including:

- Counting blessings, or noting things to be grateful for.

- 'Three good things', where the goal is to list three positive things that happened.

- Grateful self-reflection following events and their impact on self and others.

- Gratitude visits (either in person or in the form of letters not sent) to acknowledge the impact of significant people on our lives.

This section includes exercises to help you practise gratitude.

9

Choose a photo that you cherish. Write about why you're grateful for that memory.

gratitude is the memory of the heart.
- jean baptiste massieu -

trade your
expectation for
appreciation and
the world changes
for you.
- anthony robbins -

10

What do you appreciate most about the way that you live?

practising gratitude...

- Releases dopamine and serotonin, the 'happy hormones'.
- Reduces negative affect and stress.
- Affirms the good things in your life.
- Strengthens connections to others.
- Enhances life satisfaction.
- Nurtures empathy.
- Fosters forgiveness.
- Helps reduce pain.
- Increases prosocial behaviour.
- Promotes positive relationships through kind thoughts.

11

List 5
things
that you
like
about
yourself.

12

Write a letter to someone who has played an important role in your life.

(you don't have to send it!)

It's no secret that humans are social creatures. Relationships are an important source of support and essential to our wellbeing. Today, reflect on a positive relationship - one in which you feel included, understood, and cared for. Write a letter to this person expressing the impact that they've had on you.

everything we encounter can have a positive influence
in shaping our life when we adopt a lens of gratitude.
- rob martin -

it turns out
that people
who are more
socially connected
to family, to friends,
to community, are
happier, they're
physically healthier,
and they live longer
than people who
are less well
connected.

- robert j. waldinger -

13

What are some things that you are grateful for?

Train your brain to focus on positives through regular gratitude practice. Set a timer for one minute and list things that you're grateful for.

**gratitude turns what
we have into enough.**
- various origins -

14

What 3 good things happened this week?

focus on the positive things in your life
and you'll be shocked at how many more
positive things start happening.

- sophia amoruso -

the good news brigade

Doom-scrolling - we've all been there, glued to our news feed, consuming negative news event after negative news event.

Unsurprisingly, dips in mood will occur when surrounded by constant negativity. So what's the antidote? Perhaps it's time to balance the bad with some good news.

1) good news in health

We've all been touched in some way by the cruel hand of Alzheimer's disease. Well in 2022, there was a significant breakthrough with the development of a new drug to slow cognitive decline in (what is at present) an incurable disease.

Also identified were genes responsible for brain cell death, as well as seven habits we can all adopt to reduce the risk of dementia - regular exercise, healthy diet, not smoking, maintaining a healthy weight, and keeping blood pressure, cholesterol, and blood sugar levels in check.

2) good news in nature

Thanks to the Mars Coral Reef Restoration Project from the University of Exeter, marine life on an Indonesian coral reef is now thriving a decade after the devastating impact of dynamite fishing.

Additionally, given the important role that these coral reefs play in the livelihoods of locals and in protecting their homes, this is positive news indeed.

3) good news in communities

The past few years of rolling lockdowns have highlighted the importance of connections.

In response to isolation and loneliness, there has been an increase in initiatives that boost connectedness in communities:

- Community gardens not only provide fresh fruit and vegetables locally, they also promote social interaction between neighbours.

- Little street libraries are also emerging, helping to increase literacy and enhance a sense of community.

- Intergenerational playgroups mixing aged care with child care benefit the wellbeing of both groups.

Keen to tap into more good news? Why not try websites such as goodnewsnetwork.org and positive.news?

15 What are some small pleasures that put a smile on your face?

Appreciation of the small things in life elicits positive emotions. List some of these little moments that put a smile on your face. It could be soaking in a warm bath or finding rock star parking.

think
BIG THOUGHTS
but relish
small pleasures.

- h. jackson brown jnr. -

it does not
matter how
slowly you go
as long as you
do not stop.

- confucius -

you've hit the halfway mark in this 30-day journalling challenge.

keep going!

maintaining
wellbeing
in challenging
times

Looking after your wellbeing is easy when life is going well. What's harder is doing so during challenging times.

Adversity can be hard. But even in tough times you can still care for your wellbeing by:

- Learning as a result of failure.
- Becoming more resilient due to tough times.
- Noticing and appreciating the silver linings amidst dark clouds.
- Practising gratitude for what you have.

Importantly, it's not about being happy at all times, even in difficult situations. This focus on being positive can become toxic when you deny negative feelings that you may be experiencing.

This next section looks ways to boost wellbeing and resilience in challenging times.

the shadow is the greatest teacher for how to come to the light.

- ram dass -

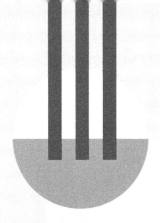

struggling to find happiness?
watch out for these happiness saboteurs

Sometimes you may struggle to feel positive even when life seems fine. During these times, it may be that happiness saboteurs are at play - a key culprit being your mindset and how you interpret things that happen to you, to others, and events in the world. Here are some ways in which mindset can sabotage wellbeing:

1) Holding a fixed mindset about happiness

It's easy to dismiss happiness as what happens to people with charmed lives - that they're born happy or have great things handed to them. However, a quick look at research into happiness and wellbeing tells us that:

- Genetic factors only make up around half of the variation in happiness. We can all take steps to increase our levels of happiness.

- Even in times of challenge and crisis, there are those who feel happy because of how they view their circumstances.

- Happiness can be actively cultivated - some ways in which this can be achieved is through shifting mindset, building social connections and positive relationships, and practising gratitude.

2) Social comparison

Ever look at others and feel bad about yourself? That you're not achieving milestones that you 'should'? Social comparison is the tendency to evaluate yourself against others, and when you come off second-best in the comparison, it's a fast track to an unhappy place. Try these whenever you feel the pang of envy:

- Step back and consider the context. You often only see a brief snapshot of someone's life, rather than the entire picture.
- Run your own race, and at your own pace. Focus on your improvements to build your sense of accomplishment (a key component in Seligman's PERMA-H model).
- Use social comparison for inspiration. What is it that you admire about this person? Is it their tenacity? Their skills? Channel this positively by setting goals that you can work towards.

3) Glass is half empty mentality

A pessimistic mindset looks for negatives, often to the point of disregarding positives that may be present. This negative headspace drives down your mood, and low mood can limit your ability to think creatively and problem-solve.

The good news is that you can actively cultivate a glass is half full mentality, and My Happy Place is designed to help you flex your positive mindset muscle.

16

Failure can be a great teacher.

Think of a past failure. How did it help you to grow?

Life can be tough.
You can find ourselves in
situations beyond our control
that bring a great deal of
distress and suffering.

anguish

difficulty
crisis
despair
challenge
woe
mishap
misery
strain
mistake
gloom
adversity
grief
regret
sorrow
misfortune
sadness
hardship
suffering

17

What's an adversity that you've overcome?

What strengths did you develop as a result of this?

anguish
difficulty crisis
despair challenge
woe
mishap misery
gleam strain mistake
adversity grief regret
sorrow misfortune
sadness hardship
suffering

you should never view your challenges
as a disadvantage.

instead, it's important for you to
understand that your experience facing
and overcoming adversity is actually
one of your biggest advantages.

- michelle obama -

For some, the workplace puts them in direct contact with suffering. First responders, nurses, doctors, psychologists, veterinarians, aid workers - these groups regularly support those facing extreme difficulties. It's no surprise that compassion fatigue and burnout are common amongst these professions.

A study of palliative care physicians (who regularly support people facing end of life) provides interesting insights into coping and resilience. These physicians reported higher levels of satisfaction and meaning as well as lower levels of burnout compared to other specialists.

What lessons can be learnt from these palliative care physicians to help you cope with adversities that you face, or face in supporting those who are suffering? Unsurprisingly, many of the answers for these physicians can be drawn from positive psychology:

- Key protective factors were finding meaning, purpose, and spirituality in their work.

- Cultivating equanimity - a state of calm and balance in response to others' difficulties, sadness, and suffering - enhanced coping.

- Focusing on the positive aspects of helping was key to building compassion satisfaction as an antidote to compassion fatigue.

- In a similar vein, focusing on others' growth in the face of hardship helped to build vicarious resilience to balance vicarious trauma.

on suffering

GRIT is the passion and perseverance for long-term goals.

- angela duckworth -

18

Think about a success that you have achieved. It could be a skill that you've mastered or an outcome that you've worked hard for.

What challenges did you encounter along the way? It may have been a lack of resources, dealing with setbacks, or coping with frustration.

Journal about what strengths helped you to overcome hurdles and stay on track to achieve your goals.

It's easy to get caught up in current challenges and discount your resilience. This exercise encourages you to reflect on a time when you've risen to the challenge.

19

Think of a challenge you're facing at the moment. List 3 obstacles lying in your way. For each obstacle, list 2 potential solutions.

1 obstacle

solutions

Focusing on the 'buts' and 'what ifs' acts to magnify setbacks. The simple act of formulating small and achievable steps to break down obstacles shows you that you are capable of doing hard things.

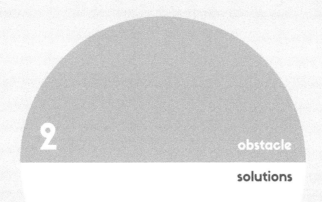

2   obstacle

solutions

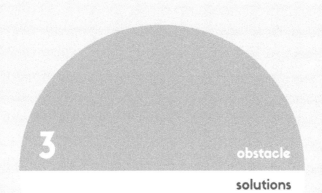

3   obstacle

solutions

identify your problems but give your power and energy to solutions. - tony robbins -

20

What would you do if you weren't constrained by anything, such as money or responsibilities?

don't limit yourself
to the skies when
there is a whole
galaxy out there.

- bianca frazier -

In challenging times when it may be tricky to get into a postive headspace, it's helpful to have ways to

↑plift

your mood. Positive emotions like joy, interest, and awe

broaden

your thought-action repertoire and act to **build** up your personal resources.

The thing about negative emotions is that they keep you stuck in old ways of thinking and stifle creativity.

If you want to tap into your well of creativity and problem solving ability, it's key to look to positive emotions.

This section therefore focuses on maximising positive mood when you need a boost.

21 List 10 things that lift you up when you feel down.

-
-
-
-
-
-
-
-
-
-

positive and negative
emotions cannot
occupy the mind at
the same time.

- napoleon hill -

Describe your
favourite childhood
memory and how it
made you feel.

22

Finding your happy place isn't just about finding happiness. There is a whole other range of positive emotions that boost our wellbeing.

One such emotion is awe. It's what you experience when faced with how vast your surroundings are, and how small you are in the grand scheme of things. You've probably experienced those awe-inducing 'wow' moments when:

- Faced with the sheer beauty and vastness of natural landscapes - mountains, canyons, lakes - that have developed over thousands of years.

- Marvelling at the miracle of life when meeting a friend's baby for the first time.

- Admiring an amazing piece of art or a mind-blowing performance.

- Stargazing upon the vast galaxy and gaining perspective on your place in space and time.

In awe of awe

This humbling awareness that you are part of something larger than yourself encourages you to connect with others and to be more present in your environment, both of which are important for wellbeing.

Frequently experiencing awe has also been linked to:

- A healthier immune system and reduced inflammatory markers.
- Increased happiness.
- Improvements in critical thinking.
- Decreased materialism.
- Increased connectedness - not just to others but also to humanity.

How can you actively cultivate awe? Adding 'moments of awe' to your journaling practice helps. Describe these 'wow' moments in fine detail, transporting yourself back to that very moment.

You may be familiar with the phrase 'to **stop and smell the roses**' but what if you turned this concept into a part of your regular routine?

The concept of **flaneuring** harks back to 19th century Paris where leisurely strollers tuned in to the finer details that many others overlooked.

Such mindful walks force a shift in focus away from the worries within, and towards the beauty in the surroundings, be it in a built environment or out in nature. Whilst you may not be in 19th century Paris you can certainly reap the benefits of flaneuring in modern day!

A spin on flaneuring is taking **awe walks** where you actively pay attention to, and connect with, your surroundings whilst **traipsing through nature**.

The benefits of an awe walk in green spaces can even be reaped in just a 30 minute stroll in an urban park - research shows that this easily-achievable step reduces worrying and improves mood.

And, following your leisurely sojourn, why not put pen to paper and **journal about your awe-filled experience**?

create experiences that leave you in awe, for these will be the highlights of your life.

- ryan blair -

23 Describe a situation in which you felt very calm or relaxed.

Close your eyes and really visualise this moment, as if you were transported back in time and place. Focus on as many elements as possible, drawing on all of your senses. Jot down as many details as you can remember.

The next time you feel stressed, refer back to what you wrote today - close your eyes and return to this relaxing situation.

Positive emotions open the door to possibilities.

24

Write about three things you'd like to work towards.

Draw inspiration from dreams that you hold dear.

how to
flourish
in life

Thus far, we've seen how wellbeing can be boosted by using your strengths and values, by increasing positive emotions, and by learning to cope in times of adversity.

In implementing these you not only maximise wellbeing - you can even flourish.

In this section we look at how to further cultivate flourishing.

25 Flourishing is to be in a fulfilling place in your life where you accomplish meaningful tasks and connect with others. Each person's path to flourishing looks different. What does flourishing look like to you?

**if a flower
can flourish in
the desert,
you can flourish
anywhere.**

- matshona dhilwayo -

What do flourishing and happiness look like around the world?

The World Happiness Report provides a snapshot of a nation's level of happiness based on six factors - per capita gross domestic product, life expectancy, freedom, social support, generosity, and the absence of corruption.

In its most recent release on the 10th anniversary of the World Happiness Report, some trends observed included:

- Globally, worry and stress eased one year on from the start of the global pandemic (though were still elevated compared to pre-pandemic levels).

- An unexpected finding was that of an increase in kindness. From the ashes of the global pandemic, levels of charity donations increased, as did volunteering - an increase of around 25% relative to pre-pandemic levels.

- Finland topped the poll as the world's happiest nation for the fifth year in a row.

- Scandinavian and European countries featured heavily in the top 10 happiest nations, with Denmark (#2), Iceland (#3), Switzerland (#4), the Netherlands (#5), Sweden (#7) and Norway (#8) also included.

- Australia (#12) and New Zealand (#10) also ranked highly.

Let's take a look at some of the nations in the 2022 World Happiness Report.

finland (#1)

Finland is blessed with breathtaking natural landscapes and a laid back way of life, but those aren't the only keys to happiness in this nation. Finland's inhabitants report high levels of safety, contentment, and trust in the government. Is it any wonder that Finland has taken out the title of the world's happiest nation for the fifth year in a row?

denmark (#2)

Denmark also regularly ranks highly in the World Happiness Index. One secret to the happiness of the Danish is the concept of **hygge**, which is about taking time away from the daily grind to focus on the good things in life and experiencing these with loved ones.

mauritius (#52)

The picturesque Mauritius is the happiest nation in Africa – unsurprisingly Mark Twain remarked, "Mauritius was made first and then heaven, heaven being copied after Mauritius".

Rounding up the top five happiest African nations were Libya (#86), Ivory Coast (#88), South Africa (#91), and Gambia (#93).

canada (#15)
+united states (#16)

Canada and the US consistently enjoy high rankings on the World Happiness Index. In addition to economic and political stability, North Americans enjoy a sense of agency and achievement, actively pursue the experience of positive affect, and also nurture their social relationships - all of which contribute to their high levels of wellbeing.

costa rica (#23)

Costa Rica topped the list of the happiest nations in Latin America, followed by Uruguay (#30), Panama (#37), Brazil (#38), Guatemala (#39), and Chile (#44).

What influences happiness in Latin America? A strong sense of family and interpersonal relationships, and the resulting levels of social support and social cohesion contribute to wellbeing and life satisfaction. The value placed on family and social connectedness is highlighted by the positive impact that having children has on happiness.

the art of being happy
lies in the power of
extracting happiness
from common things.
- henry ward beecher -

united arab emirates (#24)

The UAE appointed its first Minister of State for Happiness in 2016 to drive policy for positive social change. As part of its aim to shape generational change, the UAE established:

- The Well Schools Network, created to embed wellbeing into the school curriculum.
- The Happiness and Wellbeing Program in the Workplace, which provides employees with a happiness manual and helps employee to track their happiness and wellbeing.
- Project Purpose, to teach university students important life skills to set and achieve goals.

These initiatives are bearing fruit for the UAE and its people, setting the background for generations to come.

afghanistan (#146)

Afghanistan ranked as the least happy nation in 2022's World Happiness Index (#146), highlighting the impact that ongoing conflict can have on a nation's wellbeing. Other nations with impacted happiness levels include Lebanon (#145), Zimbabwe (#144), Rwanda (#143), and Botswana (#142).

> **happiness can change, and does change, according to the quality of the society in which people live.**
>
> **- world happiness report, 2018 -**

bhutan

Although not surveyed in the latest World Happiness Report, Bhutan (#95 in the 2021 ranking) deserves a mention for its commitment to the happiness of its people. Whilst many nations chart progress in economic terms, Bhutan developed the **Gross National Happiness (GNH) Index** which measures progress in both economic and non-economic terms spread across nine domains, including psychological wellbeing, health, education, cultural diversity and resilience, community vitality, and living standards.

japan (#54)

The Japanese concept of **ikigai** refers to a 'reason for living', a life purpose if you will, which is key to a long and happy life. We experience ikigai when we engage in actions aligned with our values, with these actions also producing a sense of accomplishment. Wellbeing researchers draw similarities between ikigai and what Martin Seligman describes as an 'engaged life', one of the three paths to happiness.

australia (#12)
+new zealand (#10)

New Zealand (#10) and Australia (#12) are the happiest nations in the Oceania region. With amazing landscapes and a relaxed lifestyle, it's no surprise that these two nations rank so highly in happiness.

nature is one of the most under-utilised treasures in life. it has the power to unburden hearts and reconnect to that inner place of peace. - janice anderson -

ingredients
for flourishing

Looking at happiness around the world it's clear that you can still flourish in challenging times. Martin Seligman outlined factors for flourishing in his PERMA model, which was later extended to incorporate a new pillar, H, focusing on physical health and its impact on wellbeing. Let's look at how the prompts in My Happy Place can help you flourish in line with the PERMA-H model.

P Regularly experiencing **positive emotions** help you flourish, and the prompts in My Happy Place help foster awe, and gratitude, and call out happiness saboteurs.

E Flexing your strengths encourages a state of flow and increases flourishing. In My Happy Place we've helped you to identify and build on these strengths to enhance **engagement**.

R Social connections and **positive relationships** are key to happiness, and we cultivate these through gratitude journalling.

M Find **meaning** and purpose in life with My Happy Place - the prompts are designed to help you explore what you value in life.

A Journalling about **accomplishments**, resilience, and grit helps to reinforce a sense of mastery and increases flourishing in life.

H My Happy Place helps you to care for your **physical health** by tuning into your body's needs using mindfulness.

List other ways in which you can flourish in life by building up each element of PERMA-H.

P

E

R

M

A

H

27 When are you in a state of flow?

Mihalyi Csikszentmihalyi defined flow as "being completely involved in an activity for its own sake. The ego falls away. Time flies. Every action, movement, and thought follows inevitably from the previous one, like playing jazz."

When are you in a state of flow? Make a plan for this week to do at least one activity in which you are totally engaged.

Engagement is one element of Martin Seligman's PERMA-H model of happiness and wellbeing. When you are fully immersed in an activity or task, the experience itself is rewarding and enriching. Live a more engaged life by identifying tasks that capture your full attention and make time to partake in these activities.

Is happiness hardwired?

did you know?

Is happiness hardwired? Well... yes and no. As it turns out, the answer depends on how you look at the puzzle.

Studies of **enduring levels of happiness**, based on twin and family studies, suggest that around 50% of variation in happiness is due to genes. This supports the idea of a set range of happiness, but clearly there are other factors that contribute to enduring levels of happiness.

However, when considering **happiness as a momentary state** (for example, positive affect), genes appears to have little influence.

The bottom line? We can all take action to boost our happiness, be it just in the moment or at a more enduring level.

being happy isn't having everything in your life be perfect.

maybe it's about stringing together all the little things.

- ann brashares -

Let's dive deeper into what makes up our enduring levels of happiness. Martin Seligman, author of Authentic Happiness, offers up this equation:

(enduring level of happiness) (set range) (circumstances) (voluntary variables under our control)

Breaking these down:

- S = the set range of happiness. This is influenced by our genes, meaning that you unfortunately can't do much to shift this variable.

- C = those external circumstances that have a meaningful impact on happiness. Seligman identified positive social connections, having religious faith, and being financially comfortable as supporting happiness. It also helps to avoid negative events. Interestingly, this variable is estimated to contribute only around 8-15% of variance in happiness.

- V = those variables under our control that we can work on to create a sustainable change in happiness (rather than just momentary improvements). Seligman encourages us all to build positive emotions by:

  - Reflecting on the past to cultivate satisfaction, pride, serenity, and contentment.

  - Experiencing the present through mindful awareness to foster joy, pleasure, flow, and awe.

  - Looking forward to the future and increasing hope, faith, and optimism.

a
happier

throughout
the ages

Researchers have long tried to pinpoint links between happiness and other demographics. One striking finding has been the relationship between happiness and age.

happiness varies with age following a **U-shaped** pattern declining from early adulthood until it hits **'peak unhappiness'** during **mid life** before rising again.

How universal is this finding? A 2017 analysis of happiness markers in 46 countries found this U-shaped curve to hold true in 44 countries. A more recent study in 2021 of 145 countries also replicated this U-shaped finding.

Over the next few pages we'll take a closer look at the relationship between happiness and age.

are we inevitably destined for middle-aged doom and gloom?

The U-shaped relationship between happiness and age may look gloomy in midlife, but it's helpful to remember some important points:

consider the context

Each life stage has its challenges. On the next page the unique challenges from early adulthood through to late adulthood (the period of the U-shape curve) show that it's often during midlife that multiple responsibilities pile up. These may include parenting children, caring for parents, increased responsibilities at work, and health issues. Midlife may also be a period for reflecting on meaning in life and facing mortality.

theory of relativity

Unhappiness may peak in midlife, but consider that this is relative to other stages in life - that is, the overall levels of happiness may still be quite high. However, if you're only focusing on the negatives, then negative feelings will naturally follow. Which leads us to the next point...

cruise control

It's helpful to remember that happiness can be increased through intentional practice. Even if you're feeling overwhelmed by your circumstances, you can still find the silver linings and feel comforted by your resilience.

twenties + thirties

Why might happiness start to decline in our early twenties? This is a time of rapid growth and development in the professional, financial, and personal realms. Pressure in these areas (from work woes, debt, and 'adulting') lowers wellbeing and happiness.

In the personal realm, friendships and relationships- and their related conflict and strain - feature heavily during this time. It's also when many start families and fertility may be a concern. Those with young families step into parental responsibilities, juggling these in addition to looking after finances, career, and home. Alongside these life events and role changes may emerge significant identity shifts that affect happiness.

forties + fifties

These years of peak unhappiness are characteristically marked by significant responsibilities. Often referred to as the 'sandwich generation', this middle-aged cohort commonly provides support (financial, emotional, physical) to both children and parents.

It's also an age when the optimism of youth starts to fade. Many begin thinking about winding down careers and planning for retirement. Physically they are faced with an ageing body, reduced capabilities, and mortality. Social supports may also dwindle due to becoming empty nesters or having friends with busy lives who have limited opportunities for socialising.

sixties and beyond

Happiness starts to increase again during this stage, likely reflecting reduced responsibilities in life. In spite of this, challenges faced in this age group includes social isolation and financial uncertainty. On a positive note, it's often a time by which one has found meaning in life, which contributes to increased levels of happiness.

every age
has its happiness
and troubles.

- jeanne calment -

28

Reflect on the different stages of your life thus far.

(childhood, adolescence, early adulthood, middle adulthood, late adulthood)

For each stage, journal about:

- Your happiest moments.
- The challenges that you've faced and the resilience that you've developed.
- What you were grateful for during that time in your life.

As you reflect on the life that you've lived, tune in to how
your experiences shape who you are and what you value.

a joyful life is an individual creation that cannot be copied from a recipe.

- mihayli csikszentmihayli -

what
ingredients
make your life
uniquely
joyful?

29

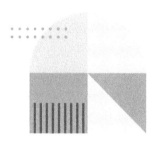

30

Think back to when you
started this journal.
What has changed?
How can you continue to
use positive psychology
in your life?

where to from here?

The past 30 days have taken you on a journey to your happy place.

Through dedication and consistency, you've carved out journalling as a daily habit. But where to next?

keep going

To maintain the benefits from these past 30 days follow these next pages to take you through the next 30 days... and beyond.

happy journalling!

if I get lost, this journal will be like a record of who I was, a trail of bread crumbs to find my way back.

- jonathan tropper -

The many faces of journalling

Journalling comes in many different forms, and variety might just be what keeps journalling interesting and keeps you motivated to maintain it as a habit. Moving forward, why not try other forms of journalling?

Art or visual journalling
For days when you're not in the mood to write, try doodling or drawing what you're feeling instead. It's still a chance to pause and reflect.

Journalling about experiences
Whether it's an awe-filled hike, a meal that you've savoured, or a life-changing holiday, journalling about experiences can transport you back to happy places.

Video or photo journalling
Journalling via videos and photos can capture the nuances and feelings of moments beyond words on a page.

Letter journalling

We've covered different types of letter journalling in My Happy Place, including a letter to your best possible self and to someone important, but why not try other types of letter journalling?

Write a letter to your present-day self. It's a great snapshot of your life as it currently is, and is something to look back on in the future.

Or, write a letter to your younger self through a compassionate lens to help you process strong feelings and forgive yourself for past regrets.

You can also write a letter to your future self to help clarify your values and guide your actions moving forward.

Stream of consciousness journalling

On days when the well of journalling prompts runs dry, you can try stream of consciousness journalling. This involves putting pen to paper about whatever springs to mind. No prompts needed – Just. Keep. Journalling.

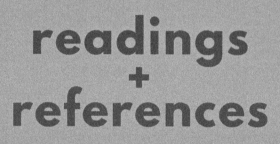
readings
+
references

references

Armenta, C.N., Fritz, M.M, Lyubormirsky, S. (2017). Functions of positive emotions: Gratitude as a motivator of self-improvement and positive change. *Emotion Review, 9*, 183-190. https://doi.org/10.1177/1754073916669596

Blanchflower, D.G. (2021). Is happiness U-shaped everywhere? Age and subjective well-being in 145 countries. *Journal of Population Economics 34*, 575-624. https://doi.org/10.1007/s00148-020-00797-z

Buettner, D., Nelson, T. & Veenhoven, R. (2020). Ways to Greater Happiness: A Delphi Study. *Journal of Happiness Studies, 21*, 2789-2806. https://doi.org/10.1007/s10902-019-00199-3

Capaldi CA, Dopko RL, Zelenski JM. (2014). The relationship between nature connectedness and happiness: a meta-analysis. *Frontiers in Psychology, 8*, 1-15. https://doi: 10.3389/fpsyg.2014.00976.

Carsley, D., & Heath, N.L., (2018). Effectiveness of mindfulness-base colouring for test anxiety in adolescents. *School Psychology International, 39*, 251-272. https://doi: 10.1177/0143034318773523

Chambers, R., Lo, B.C.Y., & Allen, N.B. (2007). The impact of intensive mindfulness training on attentional control, cognitive style, and affect. *Cognitive Therapy and Research, 32*, 302-322. https://doi.org/10.1007/s10608-007-9119-0

Chiesa, A., Calati, R., Serretti, A. (2011). Does mindfulness training improve cognitive abilities? A systematic review of neuropsychological findings. *Clinical Psychology Review, 31*, 449-464. https://doi.org/10.1016/j.cpr.2010.11.003

Clear, J. (2018). *Atomic habits: Tiny changes, remarkable results: An easy & proven way to build good habits and break bad ones.* New York: Avery.

Csikszentmihalyi, M. (1990). *Flow: The Psychology of Optimal Experience.* New York: Harper and Row.

Curry, O.S. & Rowland, L.A., van Lissa, C., Zlotowitz, S., Mcalaney, J., & Whitehouse, H. (2018). Happy to help? A systematic review and meta-analysis of the effects of performing acts of kindness on the well-being of the actor. *Journal of Experimental Social Psychology. 76*, 320-329. https://doi.org/10.1016/j.jesp.2018.02.014

Davis, D. E., Choe, E., Meyers, J., Wade, N., Varjas, K., Gifford, A., Quinn, A., Hook, J. N., Van Tongeren, D. R., Griffin, B. J., & Worthington, E. L., Jr. (2016). Thankful for the little things: A meta-analysis of gratitude interventions. *Journal of Counseling Psychology, 63*, 20-31. https://doi.org/10.1037/cou0000107

Duckworth, A. L., Peterson, C., Matthews, M. D., & Kelly, D. R. (2007). Grit: perseverance and passion for long-term goals. *Journal of Personality and Social Psychology, 92*, 1087. https://doi.org/10.1037/0022-3514.92.6.1087

Emmons, R. A., & Mishra, A. (2011). Why gratitude enhances well-being: What we know, what we need to know. In K. M. Sheldon, T. B. Kashdan, & M. F. Steger (Eds.), *Designing Positive Psychology: Taking and Moving Forward* (pp. 248-262). NY: Oxford University Press.

Fredrickson, B. L. (2001). The role of positive emotions in positive psychology: The broaden-and-build theory of positive emotions. *American Psychologist, 56*, 218-226. https://doi.org/10.1037/0003-066X.56.3.218

Galambos NL, Krahn HJ, Johnson MD, Lachman ME. The U Shape of Happiness Across the Life Course: Expanding the Discussion. *Perspectives on Psychological Science: A journal of the Association for Psychological Science, 15*, 898-912. https://doi:.org.10.1177/1745691620902428.

García-Alandete, J. (2015). Does meaning in life predict psychological wellbeing: An analysis using the Spanish versions of the purpose-in-life test and the Ryff's scales. *The European Journal of Counselling Psychology, 3*, 89-98. https://doi.org/10.5964/ejcop.v3i2.27

Geier MT, Morris J. The impact of a gratitude intervention on mental well-being during COVID-19: A quasi-experimental study of university students. Applied Psychology. Health and well-being, 14, 937-948. https://doi.org/10.1111/aphw.12359

Graham, C., & Ruiz Pozuelo, J. (2017). Happiness, stress, and age: how the U curve varies across people and places. *Journal of Population Economics 30*, 225-264. https://doi.org/10.1007/s00148-016-0611-2

Grundy, E., & Henretta, J. (2006). Between elderly parents and adult children: A new look at the intergenerational care provided by the 'sandwich generation'. *Ageing & Society, 26*, 707-722. https://doi.org/10.1017/S0144686X06004934

Guendelman, S., Medeiros, S., & Rampes, H. (2017). Mindfulness and emotion regulation: Insights from neurobiological, psychological, and clinical studies. *Frontiers in Psychology, 8*, 220. https://doi.org/10.3389/fpsyg.2017.00220

Helliwell, J.F., Layard, R., Sachs, J.D., De Neve, J-E., Aknin, L.B., & Wang, S. (2022). *World Happiness Report 2022*. New York: Sustainable Development Solutions Network powered by the Gallup World Poll data. https://worldhappiness.report/

Jans-Beken, L., Jacobs, N., Janssens, M., Peeters, S., Reijnders, J., Lechner, L., & Lataster, J. (2020). Gratitude and health: An updated review. *The Journal of Positive Psychology, 15*, 743-782. https://doi.org/10.1080/17439760.2019.1651888

Kerr, S.L., O'Donovan, A. & Pepping, C.A. (2015). Can Gratitude and Kindness Interventions Enhance Well-Being in a Clinical Sample?. *Journal of Happiness Studies 16*, 17-36. https://doi.org/10.1007/s10902-013-9492-1

Ko, K., Margolis, S., Revord, J., & Lyubomirsky, S. (2021). Comparing the effects of performing and recalling acts of kindness. The Journal of Positive Psychology, 16, 73-81. https://doi.org/10.1080/17439760.2019.1663252

Kono, S., Walker, G.J. (2020). Theorizing Ikigai or Life Worth Living Among Japanese University Students: A Mixed-Methods Approach. *Journal of Happiness Studies, 21*, 327-355. https://doi.org/10.1007/s10902-019-00086-x

Lasota, A., Tomaszek, K. & Bosacki, S. (2022). How to become more grateful? The mediating role of resilience between empathy and gratitude. *Current Psychology, 41*, 6848-6857. https://doi.org/10.1007/s12144-020-01178-1

Laaksonen, S. A. (2018). Research Note: Happiness by Age is More Complex than U-Shaped. *Journal of Happiness Studies 19*, 471-482. https://doi.org/10.1007/s10902-016-9830-1

Lavy, S., & Benish-Weisman, M. (2021). Character strengths as 'Values in Action': Linking character strengths with values theory - an exploratory study of the case of gratitude and self-transcendence. *Frontiers in Psychology, 12*, 1-9. https://doi.org/10.3389/fpsyg.2021.576189

Luo, L., Mao, J., Chen, S., Gao, W., & Yuan, J. (2021). Psychological research of awe: Definitions, functions, and application in psychotherapy. *Stress and Brain, 1*, 59-75. https://doi.org/10.26599/SAB.2020.9060003.

McMahan, D, (2022). What is flaneuring? The walking trend that will leave you relaxed and inspired. Today. https://www.today.com/health/what-flaneuring-how-can-you-take-awe-walk-t195686

McGrath, R.E. (2015). Character strengths in 75 nations: An update. *The Journal of Positive Psychology, 10*, 41-52. https://doi.org/10.1080/17439760.2014.888580.

Mikkelsen, K., Stojanovska, L., Polenakovic, M., Bosevski, M., & Apostolopoulos, V. (2017). Exercise and mental health. *Maturitas, 106*, 48-56. https://doi.org/10.1016/j.maturitas.2017.09.003

National Program for Happiness and Wellbeing. https://www.hw.gov.ae/en/initiatives/1

Neff, K., & McGehee, P. (2010). Self-compassion and psychological resilience among adolescents and young adults. *Self and Identity, 9*, 225-240. https://doi.org/10.1080/15298860902979307

Nelson, S. K., Layous, K., Cole, S. W., & Lyubomirsky, S. (2016). Do unto others or treat yourself? The effects of prosocial and self-focused behavior on psychological flourishing. Emotion, 16, 850-861. https://doi.org/10.1037/emo0000178

Nes, R.B., Roysamb, E. (2017). Happiness in behaviour genetics: An update on heritability and changeability. *Journal of Happiness Studies, 18*, 1533-1552. https://doi.org/10.1007/s10902-016-9871-6

Norrish, J.M., Williams, P., O'Connor, M., & Robinson, J. (2013). An applied framework for positive education. *International Journal of Wellbeing, 3*, 147-161. doi:10.5502/ijw.v3i2.2

Pascoe MC, Thompson DR, Jenkins ZM, Ski CF. (2017). Mindfulness mediates the physiological markers of stress: Systematic review and meta-analysis. *Journal of Psychiatric Research, 95*, 156-178. https://doi.org/10.1016/j.jpsychires.2017.08.004.

Peterson, C., & Seligman, M.E.P. (2004). *Character strengths and virtues: A handbook and classification.* New York: Oxford University Press and Washington, DC: American Psychological Association.

Pritchard, A., Richardson, M., Sheffield, D. et al. (2020). The relationship between nature connectedness and eudaimonic well-being: A meta-analysis. *Journal of Happiness Studies, 21*, 1145-1167. https://doi.org/10.1007/s10902-019-00118-6

Proctor, C., Maltby, J., & Linley, P. (2010). Strengths use as a predictor of wellbeing and health-related quality of life. *Journal of Happiness Studies, 12*, 153-169. https://doi.org/10.1007/s10902-009-9181-2

Rowland, L. & Curry, O.S. (2019) A range of kindness activities boost happiness. *The Journal of Social Psychology, 159*, 340-343. https://doi.org/10.1080/00224545.2018.1469461

Seligman, M.E.P. (1991). *Learned Optimism: How to Change Your Mind and Your Life.* New York, NY: Pocket Books

Schotanus-Dijkstra, M., Pieterse, M.E., Drossaert, C.H.C. et al. (2016). What factors are associated with flourishing? Results from a large representative national sample. *Journal of Happiness Studies 17*, 1351-1370. https://doi.org/10.1007/s10902-015-9647-3

Segal, Z.V., Williams, J.M.G., Teasdale, J.D. (2002). *Mindfulness-based cognitive therapy for depression: A new approach to preventing relapse.* Guilford Press.

Seligman, M.E.P. (2002). *Authentic happiness: Using the new positive psychology to realise your potential for lasting fulfilment.* New York: Free Press.

Seligman, M. (2010, October). *Flourishing: Positive psychology and positive interventions.* Paper presented at The Tanner Lectures on Human Values, University of Michigan, MI. Retrieved from http://www.isbm.at/pics/Flourish_Seligman.pdf

Seligman, M.E.P., & Csikszentmihalyi, M. (2000). Positive psychology: An introduction. *American Psychologist, 55*, 5-14. https://doi.org/10.1037/0003-066X.55.1.5

Steger, M.F., Oishi, S. & Kashdan, T.B. (2009) Meaning in life across the life span: Levels and correlates of meaning in life from emerging adulthood to older adulthood. *The Journal of Positive Psychology, 4*, 43-52, DOI: 10.1080/17439760802303127

Sturm, V. E., Datta, S., Roy, A. R. K., Sible, I. J., Kosik, E. L., Veziris, C. R., Chow, T. E., Morris, N. A., Neuhaus, J., Kramer, J. H., Miller, B. L., Holley, S. R., & Keltner, D. (2022). Big smile, small self: Awe walks promote prosocial positive emotions in older adults. *Emotion, 22*, 1044-1058. https://doi.org/10.1037/emo0000876

Toepfer, S.M., Cichy, K., & Peters, P. (2012). Letters of gratitude: Further evidence for author benefits. *Journal of Happiness Studies, 13*, 187-201. https://doi.org/10.1007/s10902-011-9257-7

Xiang, Y., Yuan, R. (2021). Why Do People with High Dispositional Gratitude Tend to Experience High Life Satisfaction? A Broaden-and-Build Theory Perspective. *Journal of Happiness Studies, 22*, 2485-2498. https://doi.org/10.1007/s10902-020-00310-z

Wood, A.M., Froh, J.J., & Geraghty, A.W.A. (2010). Gratitude and well-being: A review and theoretical integration. *Clinical Psychology Review, 30*, 890-905. https://doi.org/10.1016/j.cpr.2010.03.005

the capacity
to learn is a gift;
the ability to learn is
a skill; the willingness
to learn is a
choice.

- brian herbert -

additional resources

Keen to continue living your best life? Below are some additional resources that we recommend to help you on your way.*

books

Brown, B. (2010). The gifts of imperfection. MN: Hazelden.

Csikszentmihalyi, M. (2009). Flow: The psychology of optimal experience. Harper and Row.

Duckworth, A. (2016). Grit: The power of passion and perseverance. Scriner/Simon & Schuster.

Dweck, C. (2017), Mindset: Changing the way you think to fulfil your potential. NY: Random House.

Lyubomirsky, S. (2008). The how of happiness: A new approach to getting the life you want.NYL Penguin Press.

Neff, K., & Germer, C. (2018). The mindful self-compassion workbook. A proven way to accept yourself, build inner strength, and thrive. NY: Guildford Press.

Owen, E. (2019). The art of flaneuring. How to wander with intention and discover a better life. Simon & Schuster.

Puddicombe, A. (2016). The headspace guide to meditation and mindfulness: How mindfulness can change your life in ten minutes a day. NY: St Martin's Griffin.

Seligman, M.E.P. (2002). Authentic happiness: Using the new positive psychology to realise your potential for lasting fulfilment. New York: Free Press.

Seligman, M. E. P. (2013). Flourish. Simon & Schuster.

websites

www.greatergood.berkeley.edu - Greater Good Science Center, University of Berkeley
www.positivepsychology.com
www.posproject.org/character-strengths - The Positivity Project
www.ppc.sas.upenn.edu - Positive Psychology Centre, University of Pennsylvania
www.viacharacter.org - VIA Character Strengths Survey

apps

Action for happiness
Calm
Happify
Headspace

*We have no control over the content of any external sources, and it is the responsibility of the reader to make their own decisions about the accuracy, currency, reliability and correctness of the information found.

hey there!

**We hope My Happy Place has
taken you to a place of bliss!**

There's more to discover in the world of wellbeing,
mental health, and performance so head on over
to our resources page at
theskillcollective.com/resources

- Planet Burnout
- Social Set
- Speaking Volumes
- 14-day Wellbeing Challenge
- Resource Library of tip sheets
- Productive Life Planner

THE SKILL COLLECTIVE

We help individuals and
organisations build skills for
better wellbeing, mental health,
and performance.

TheSkillCollective.com